Grammar

Grade 2

Reading and writing are the cornerstones of education. The basics of these skills include reading comprehension and a working knowledge of grammar and spelling. Language class, in which students develop their foundation of English, should be an enjoyable, educational experience for all students. This is possible, however, only if students are conscious of steady progress in their written language, and if they understand what they are doing.

This *Grammar Grade 2* book is part of a *Basics First* series that has been designed to help students succeed in grammar usage. The activities were created to help students feel confident about their grammar skills and help them understand the steps involved in learning these skills.

The pages have been arranged in an easy-to-follow format. This format allows the teacher to choose from a variety of second-grade grammar skills that are presented in an interesting, relevant, and age-appropriate manner. Each skill begins with rules. These skills are followed by intensive practice with interesting information. The skills included are those that every second-grade student should possess in order to express himself or herself confidently in spoken and written English.

With more emphasis being placed on the traditional basic subjects, it is easy to understand the vital role grammar plays in everyone's life. It has become clear how important the teaching of grammar is in helping students to become confident in their English usage.

This book can be used alone or as an integral part of any language program. It can also be used in conjunction with literature-based programs to provide students with the benefits of a well-rounded English language education.

Bears, Bears, Bears

Name _____

A **sentence** is a group of words that tells what someone or something is or does. Underline the words below that are not sentences. Add words to make them sentences.

Bears are big animals. Thick fur. They have small eyes and small ears. Bears walk on their four large feet.

Bears eat meat and many other foods. They hunt mice and squirrels. They eat berries, acorns, and nuts. Bears also.

Mother bears have between one and four cubs. Usually have twins. Bear cubs stay in the den for about two months.

There are many kinds of bears. Brown bears largest. Polar bears are also very large. They live in the Arctic. Sun bears are small.

Try This! Write a sentence that tells about the colors of bears.

2

Skating Fun

Name _____

Write the words below
in the correct order to
make sentences.

1. best My friend Denise. is

   _____

2. very is a She good ice skater.

   _____

3. Denise turns. can fancy do

   _____

4. teaching to me She is how skate.

   _____

5. ice. I on the Sometimes fall hard

   _____

6. like I to backwards. skate

   _____

7. skating We fun have together.

   _____

Try This! What clues helped you put the sentences in the correct order?

3

Places to Go

Name _____

The **subject** part of a sentence tells
whom or what the sentence is about.
Read each sentence. Write a subject for it.

1. _____

_____ went

to the art museum.

2. _____

_____

is my favorite artist.

3. _____

_____ would like

hiking in the forest.

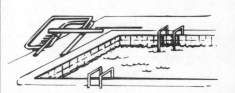

4. _____

_____ live

in the forest.

5. _____

_____ is

a good swimmer.

6. _____

_____ is

where I like to swim.

7. _____

_____ are planning

a vacation.

8. _____

_____ is

where I want to go.

9. _____

is a good place to

go to on a rainy day.

 **Try This!** Write a sentence that has a friend of yours as the subject.

4

FS-30041 Grammar

Name _____

The **predicate** part of a sentence tells what the subject does or is.

Write a predicate to finish each sentence.

1. My friend and I _____

_____

2. A scary-looking spider _____

_____

3. Three tiny ladybugs _____

4. My family _____

5. The blue whale _____

6. Valentine's Day _____

7. Snowflakes _____

8. That calculator _____

9. Our favorite playground _____

_____

10. My very best friend _____

_____

_____

Try This! Write a sentence telling your favorite thing to do. Underline the predicate.

Pretty Strange Pets

Name _____

A sentence has two main parts:
1. The **subject** tells whom or what the sentence is about.
2. The **predicate** tells what is happening.

Read the subjects and predicates below. Mix and match them to make four silly sentences. Write them below.

Subjects
Mary's boa
Grandma's fish
That spotted pony
The gerbil family
My new puppy
Todd's rabbit
Their parrot

Predicates
sings "Happy Birthday."
can do a back flip.
goes to school.
plays the piano.
does the dishes for me.
watches too much TV.
is learning to ride a bike.

1. _____

_____

2. _____

_____

3. _____

_____

4. _____

_____

_____

 **Try This!**   Write another predicate to add to the box.

6

Flower Fun

Name _____

A **telling sentence** tells you something. It begins with a capital letter and ends with a period (**.**).

Color this picture. Use it to write four telling sentences.

Example:
A flower is a plant.

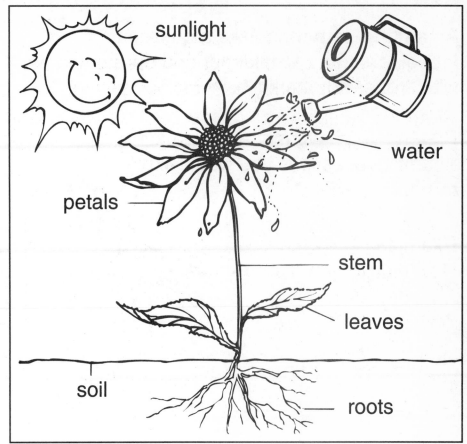

sunlight

water

petals

stem

leaves

soil

roots

1. _____

_____

2. _____

_____

3. _____

_____

4. _____

_____

Try This!   Write a telling sentence about a flower you like.

FS-30041 Grammar

A Talking Tiger

Name _____

An **asking sentence** asks a question. It begins with a capital letter and ends with a question mark (**?**).

Pretend you have met a talking tiger. Write five questions you would like to ask it.

Example:
How did you learn to talk?

1. _____
   _____

2. _____
   _____

3. _____
   _____

4. _____
   _____

5. _____
   _____

Try This!   Write a question the tiger might ask you.

Annie Jump Cannon

Name _____

Read each sentence.

If it is a telling sentence, write **T** and the missing period.

If it is an asking sentence, write **A** and the missing question mark.

A 1. Do you know who Annie Jump Cannon was_?_

T 2. She lived about 100 years ago_·_

___ 3. Annie Jump Cannon was an astronomer__

___ 4. Do you know what that is__

___ 5. An astronomer is a scientist who studies the sky__

___ 6. Annie loved to watch the stars when she was little__

___ 7. She would sit up on the roof of her house__

___ 8. Do you ever watch the stars at night__

___ 9. Can you find the Big Dipper in the sky__

___ 10. Annie went to college to learn more about space__

___ 11. She would study the sky by looking through a telescope__

___ 12. Have you ever used a telescope__

___ 13. Annie Jump Cannon became an important astronomer__

___ 14. She created a way of grouping stars by the light they make__

Try This! Write a sentence telling what you want to be when you grow up.

Wow!

Name _____

An **exclamation** is a sentence that shows strong feeling.
It begins with a capital letter and ends with an exclamation mark (**!**).
Read each setting. Write an exclamation you might say.

1. Your story won first prize.

_____

2. You spilled paint all over.

_____

3. Your dog wet your bed.

_____

4. Your hamster had its babies.

_____

5. You broke a window.

_____

6. Your friend gets to sleep over.

_____

 **Try This!** Read aloud your exclamations using expression in your voice.

At the Dinosaur Museum

Name _____

Read what the children below said on their field trip.
Write the missing period (**.**) at the end of telling sentences.
Write the missing question mark (**?**) at the end of asking sentences.
Write the missing exclamation mark (**!**) at the end of exclamations.

Wow, look how big it is

How do they know dinosaurs didn't drag their tails

Machines make these dinosaur models move

Which was the biggest dinosaur

That dinosaur is going to get you. Watch out

Paleontologists are scientists who study dinosaurs

Could we go on a dinosaur dig

This is a claw of a tyrannosaurus

What did stegosaurus use its plates for

Thank you

Try This!

Write a telling sentence, a question, and an exclamation you might say at a dinosaur museum.

11

Mixed-Up Commands

Name _____

A **command** is a sentence that tells
someone to do something. It begins with
a capital letter and ends with a period.

Jason and Sam created a robot. They are
giving their friend Joe commands to see
if it works. Unscramble the words below
to create the commands.

1. office Go our to

_____

2. the Open door red

_____

3. shortest the Find robot

_____

4. blue its knob for Look

_____

5. knob the three Turn times

_____

6. to robot Tell the us to come

_____

 Try This! Write a command you would give the robot.

Nouns at the Beach

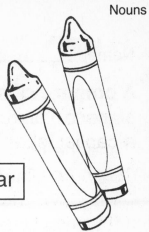

Name _____

A **noun** names a person, place, or thing.

Find the nouns listed below in the picture. Color them.

| birds | sailboats | clouds | girls | umbrellas | Snack Bar |

Then write four more nouns you see.

_____   _____

_____   _____

 Try This!   Make a list of nouns you can touch from where you are sitting.

13   FS-30041 Grammar

Busy Butterflies

Name _____

A **proper noun** names a special person, place, or thing. It begins with a capital letter.

Read the nouns on the butterfly wings. Color the wings that have proper nouns.

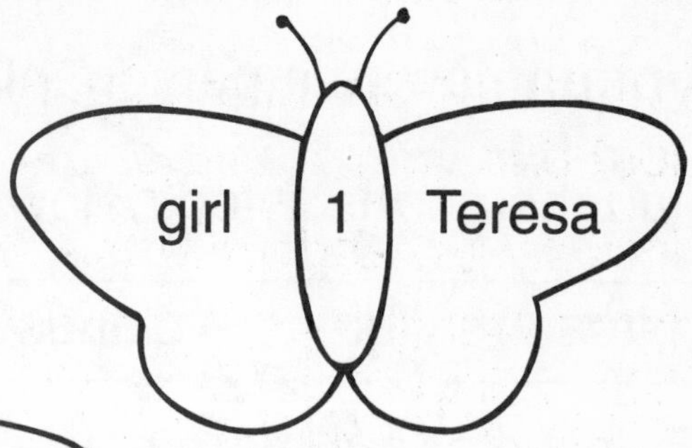

girl | 1 | Teresa

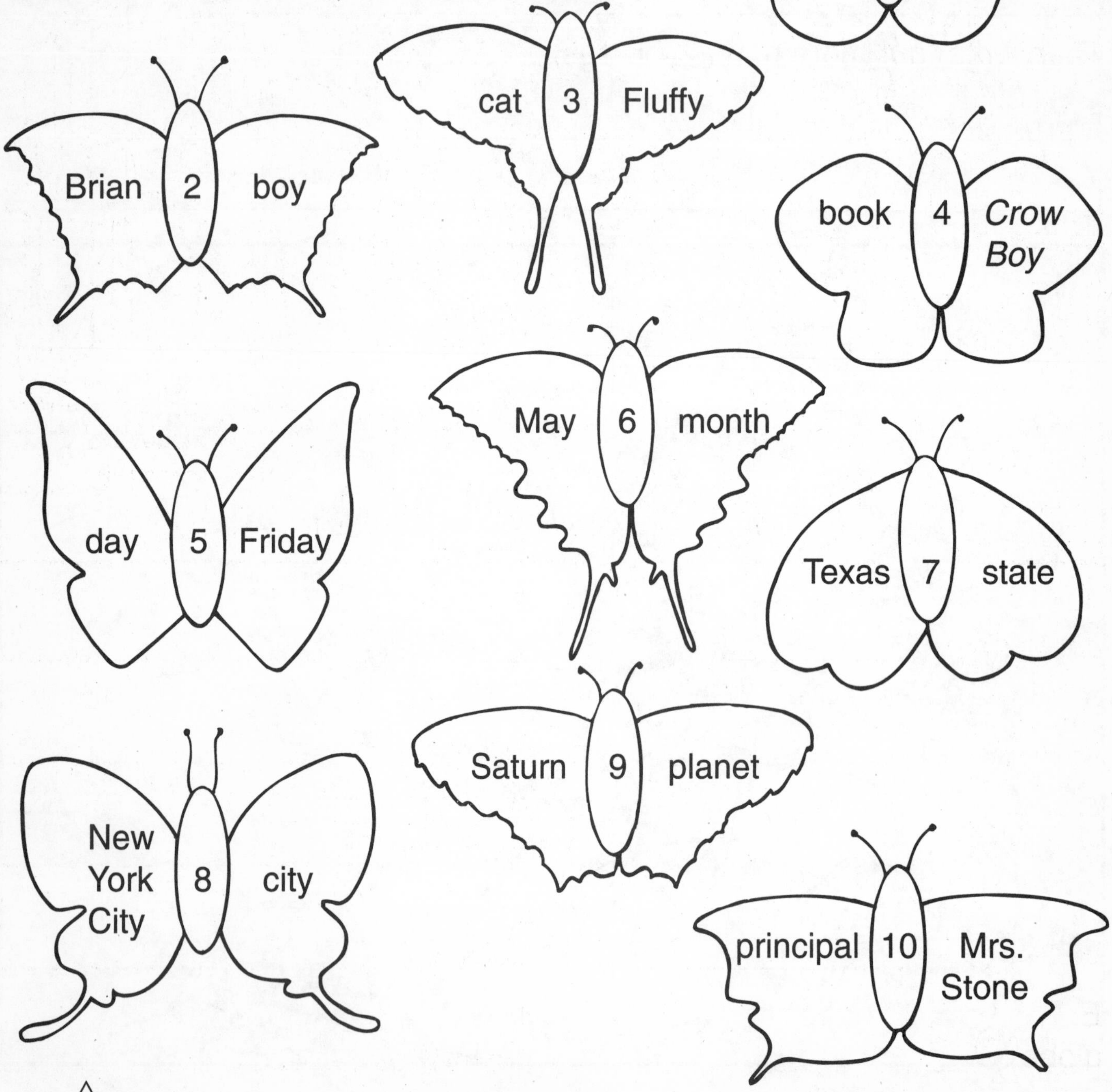

Brian | 2 | boy

cat | 3 | Fluffy

book | 4 | *Crow Boy*

day | 5 | Friday

May | 6 | month

Texas | 7 | state

New York City | 8 | city

Saturn | 9 | planet

principal | 10 | Mrs. Stone

Try This! Write a proper noun to match these words: *school, friend, pet.*

Find, Count, and Write

Name _____

A **plural noun** names more than one person, place, or thing.
Most end with the letter **s**.

Find, count, and write the nouns below. Add an **s** to make them plural.

A.
chair _5 chairs_____

B.
desk _____

C.
rabbit _____

D.
book _____

E.
globe _____

F.
crayon _____

G.
pencil _____

H.
computer _____

I.
clock _____

J.
plant _____

 Try This! Write a sentence telling how many chairs are in your room.

15

FS-30041 Grammar

Match Them Up

Name _____

A **plural noun** names more than one person, place, or thing. Most nouns are made plural by adding the letter **s**. But the nouns on this page are different.

Draw lines to match each noun to its plural.

One	More Than One	One	More Than One
fox	boxes	party	babies
ax	foxes	city	leaves
box	buses	baby	parties
bus	axes	leaf	cities
dress	lunches	wolf	elves
kiss	dresses	elf	wolves
lunch	kisses	child	women
peach	inches	man	moose
inch	bushes	woman	men
bush	ashes	moose	children
wish	peaches	deer	sheep
ash	wishes	sheep	deer

Try This! If a word ends in *x, s, ch,* or *sh,* how do you make it plural?

16

FS-30041 Grammar

A Heat Experiment

Name _____

bowls minute
cubes seconds
heat   spoon
friends spoons

Proofread the story below. Find and underline the nouns that are wrong. Write each one correctly on the line. Use the words from the bowl.

1. _____ Yesterday my three friend and I did a science

2. _____ experiment. We wanted to find out if heats travels

through some things better than others.

3. _____ First we found three spoons. One spoons was

metal, one was plastic, and one was wooden. Then

4. _____ we got two bowl. We filled one with cold water and

5. _____ lots of ice cube. My mom filled the other one with

hot water.

6. _____ We put all the spoon in the bowl of hot water.

7. _____ Then we waited for thirty second. We felt the spoons

to see if they were warm. The metal spoon was the

warmest. Next we put all the spoons in the bowl of

8. _____ ice water. This time we waited for one minutes.

Which spoon do you think was the coldest?

Try This! Write how you knew one of the nouns was wrong.

FS-30041 Grammar

Verbs at the Circus

Name _____

A **verb** is an action word.

Find the pictures that match the verbs below. Color them.

| swings | balance | drinking | step | bow | follows |

Then write four more verbs that match the picture.

_____   _____

_____   _____

Try This!   Write a sentence that tells what you would like to do at a circus. Underline the verb.

⟨18⟩

A Penguin Puppet

Name _____

Am, is, and *are* are special verbs.
They are not action words.
They tell about someone or something.

Use **is** with one person, place, or thing.
Use **are** with more than one or with the word *you.*
Use **am** with the word *I.*

Mike is making his penguin puppet speak.
Fill in the correct verb—**am, is,** or **are**—in each sentence below.

1. I _____ a penguin.

2. My name _____ Waddles.

3. I _____ from Antarctica.

4. Antarctica _____ south of here.

5. My friends _____ still there.

6. We _____ good swimmers and divers.

7. _____ you a good swimmer?

8. Penguins _____ birds.

9. But a penguin _____ not a flying bird.

10. I _____ a waddling bird.

Try This! Draw a picture of yourself holding a puppet. Write a caption showing what the puppet is saying. Use one of the following verbs: *am, is,* or *are.*

19

FS-30041 Grammar

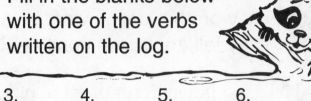

All About Raccoons

Name _____

Fill in the blanks below with one of the verbs written on the log.

1.	2.	3.	4.	5.	6.	7.	8.
is	lives	makes	hunts	eats	uses	sleeps	has
are	live	make	hunt	eat	use	sleep	have

1. A raccoon _____ a mammal.

2. Some raccoons _____ in forests.

3. They _____ their den in a hollow log or a tree.

4. Raccoons _____ at night.

5. They _____ fish, frogs, nuts, fruit, eggs, and seeds.

6. A raccoon _____ its strong claws for climbing.

7. In cold places, raccoons _____ a lot in winter.

8. Baby raccoons do not _____ rings on their tails when they are born.

 Try This! Write a question you have about raccoons. Circle the verb.

20

FS-30041 Grammar

A Past Tense Puzzle

Name _____

Some verbs tell what happened in the past. They often end in **ed**.

Read each verb. In the puzzle, write the past tense of the verb.

Across
1. trick
5. sail
7. spell
9. want
12. look
13. need

Down
2. end
3. ask
4. miss
6. plant
8. add
9. work
10. learn
11. help

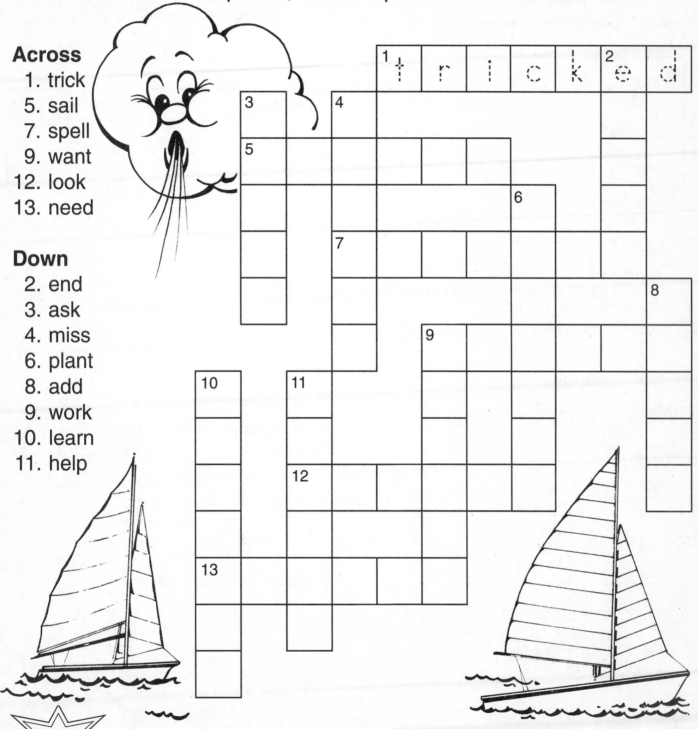

Try This! Write three more past tense verbs that end with *ed*.

21

Past Tense Match-up

Name _____

Not all verbs that show past time end in **ed**.
Draw lines to match up the present tense
and past tense verbs.

Today I...	Yesterday I...
write	thought
read	wrote
think	said
say	read

Today I...	Yesterday I...
go	flew
run	ran
fly	went
swim	stood
ride	swam
stand	rode

Today I...	Yesterday I...
eat	saw
drink	heard
see	ate
hear	drank
have	lost
lose	had

Today I...	Yesterday I...
give	took
take	made
make	left
get	gave
leave	came
come	got

Try This! Write three
sentences using
verbs from this page.

FS-30041 Grammar

Leaved or Left?

Name _____

Have you read any of Barbara Park's books about Junie B. Jones? Junie B. is a funny kindergartner who uses the wrong words a lot when she's speaking.

Read the sentences below. They are what Junie B. sounds like when she is telling about a great day. Circle the past tense verb that is wrong. Choose the correct verb from the bus. Write it on the line.

drew	made	sang
gave	put	sat
got	ran	told
left	rode	wrote

_____ 1. I leaved my house.

_____ 2. I rided the bus to school.

_____ 3. I getted off the bus like a lady.

_____ 4. I runned to my class.

_____ 5. I singed "America the Beautiful."

_____ 6. I maked a picture.

_____ 7. I drawed it really good.

_____ 8. I writed my name neatly.

_____ 9. I gived it to my teacher.

_____ 10. She putted a star on it.

_____ 11. I telled Jim that my picture was the best.

_____ 12. I sitted down and smiled.

Junie B.

Try This! Write a sentence telling about a book you read that you liked.

23

Wacky Wibbles

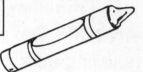

Name _____

An **adjective** is a word that describes a person, place, or thing.

Find Wibbles in the picture that match the adjectives below. Color them.

tall	round	bumpy	happy	sad	young

Then write four more adjectives that match the picture.

_____   _____

_____   _____

Try This!   Draw a Wibble that is blue, short, silly, and square.

◇24◇ FS-30041 Grammar

An Adjective Game

Name _____

Play the game below with a partner. You will need a coin. Listen for directions.

An **adjective** is a word that tells about a person, place, or thing.

Smart, happy, big, red, cold, metal, and round are all adjectives.

Start

Finish

STOP

Teacher: Give students the following directions: 1. Cut out a square from scrap paper and color it to make your game piece. 2. Taking turns, flip a coin to move. 3. If it's heads, move ahead two spaces and name two adjectives that describe the picture you landed on. If it's tails, move ahead three spaces and name three adjectives that describe the picture you landed on. 4. If you both agree your adjectives are correct, you can stay on that space, and your turn is over. If you agree your adjectives are wrong, move back one space, and your turn is over. 5. The first player to reach Finish wins.

25

Short, Shorter, Shortest

Name _____

Adjectives that compare two things often end in **er**.
Adjectives that compare three or more things often end in **est**.
Draw lines to match up the adjectives below.

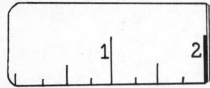 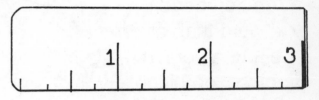

One	Two	Three or more
short	taller	slowest
tall	slower	shortest
slow	shorter	fastest
fast	later	tallest
nice	faster	nicest
late	hotter	biggest
hot	sadder	latest
big	nicer	saddest
sad	bigger	hottest
happy	funnier	messiest
funny	messier	happiest
messy	happier	funniest

Try This! Choose a set of adjectives such as *happy, happier,* and *happiest.* Draw and label three pictures to match.

FS-30041 Grammar

Bugs, Bugs, Bugs

Name _____

A and *an* are special adjectives called **articles**.

• Use **an** if the next word starts with a vowel sound.
• Use **a** if the next word starts with a consonant sound.

     Examples: **an** insect   **a** bug

Bobby made a list of insects he has seen in books. Complete the list below by adding **a** or **an** before each insect.

1. _____ ant

2. _____ ladybug

3. _____ mosquito

4. _____ firefly

5. _____ cricket

6. _____ grasshopper

7. _____ praying mantis

8. _____ earwig

9. _____ termite

10. _____ aphid

11. _____ monarch butterfly

12. _____ orange sulfur butterfly

13. _____ luna moth

14. _____ Isabella tiger moth

15. _____ underwing moth

16. _____ boll weevil

17. _____ house fly

18. _____ wasp

19. _____ honeybee

20. _____ bumblebee

Try This! Write a sentence about an insect you have seen. Use *a* or *an* in your sentence.

     27   FS-30041 Grammar

Pronoun Pictures

Name _____

A **noun** names a person, place, or thing.
A **pronoun** is a word that can take the place of a noun.
I, you, he, she, it, we, and *they* are all pronouns.

Look at each picture.
Write the matching pronoun from the pencil.

I
he
she
it
we
they

1. _____

2. _____

3. _____

4. _____

5. _____

6. _____

7. _____

8. _____

Draw
yourself
here.

→

9. _____

10. _____

Draw a
friend and
yourself
here.

←

 Try This!   Choose three pronouns. Write each one in a sentence.

28   FS-30041 Grammar

A Costume Party

Name _____

The **pronouns** *you, me, him, her, it, us,* and *them*
take the place of a person, place, or thing.
They follow action words or words like *to, of,* and *for.*

her   it
him   us
me   them

Fill in each blank with a pronoun from the balloon
that takes the place of the underlined words.

1. <u>My family and I</u> went to a big party at my Aunt Marsha's house.

   She told _____ to wear our costumes.

2. My cousin Jonah's <u>costume</u> was a giant tooth.

   He made _____ out of cardboard.

3. Jonah's friends <u>Annie and Kim</u> came as a horse.

   Aunt Marsha gave _____ an award for best team costume.

4. <u>I</u> came as a frog.

   My parents took a picture of _____.

5. My friend <u>Dave</u> was a dinosaur.

   I helped _____ carry his tail.

6. <u>Aunt Marsha</u> was a cactus.

   I asked _____ if she got tired holding up her arms.

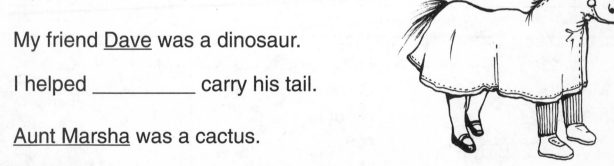

Try This!   Write a sentence that has the pronoun *you* after one of the
following words: *to, for,* or *with.*

29

FS-30041 Grammar

Meet Mousie

Name _____

An **adverb** describes an action.
Most adverbs end in **ly.**

Choose an adverb from the box
to answer each question.

Adverb Box

quickly	quietly	neatly
slowly	loudly	sloppily
carefully	happily	badly
proudly	sadly	well

1. How does Mousie run?

_____

2. How does Mousie sing?

_____

3. How does Mousie write?

_____

4. How does Mousie draw?

_____

5. How does Mousie play?

_____

6. How does Mousie work?

_____

7. How does Mousie march?

_____

8. How does Mousie read?

_____

9. How does Mousie ride?

_____

Try This! Write a sentence about yourself using one of the adverbs.

30

Answers

Page 2
Underlined sections of sentences should be rewritten as complete sentences.
<u>Thick fur.</u>
<u>Bears also.</u>
<u>Usually have twins.</u>
<u>Brown bears largest.</u>

Page 3
1. My best friend is Denise.
2. She is a very good ice skater.
3. Denise can do fancy turns.
4. She is teaching me how to skate.
5. Sometimes I fall on the hard ice. *or* Sometimes I fall hard on the ice.
6. I like to skate backwards.
7. We have fun skating together.

Page 4
Answers will vary but all should be subjects so that the sentences are finished.

Page 5
Answers will vary but all should be predicates so that the sentences are finished.

Page 6
Answers will vary but all should be silly sentences made by matching up the subjects and predicates.

Page 7
Answers will vary but all should be declarative sentences about the flower.

Page 8
Answers will vary but all five should be a question relating to a tiger.

Page 9
1. A ?
2. T .
3. T .
4. A ?
5. T .
6. T .
7. T .
8. A ?
9. A ?
10. T .
11. T .
12. A ?
13. T .
14. T .

Page 10
Answers will vary but all should be written exclamations.

Page 11
Wow, look how big it is!
How do they know dinosaurs didn't drag their tails?
Machines make these dinosaur models move.
Which was the biggest dinosaur?
Watch out!
Paleontologists are scientists who study dinosaurs.
Could we go on a dinosaur dig?
This is a claw of a tyrannosaurus.
What did stegosaurus use its plates for?
Thank you!

Page 12
1. Go to our office.
2. Open the red door.
3. Find the shortest robot.
4. Look for its blue knob.
5. Turn the knob three times.
6. Tell the robot to come to us.

Page 13
The birds, sailboats, clouds, umbrellas, Snack Bar, and girls should be colored. Written nouns will vary.

Page 14
1. Teresa
2. Brian
3. Fluffy
4. *Crow Boy*
5. Friday
6. May
7. Texas
8. New York City
9. Saturn
10. Mrs. Stone

Page 15
A. 5 chairs
B. 3 desks
C. 9 rabbits
D. 2 books
E. 2 globes
F. 3 crayons
G. 2 pencils
H. 2 computers
I. 2 clocks
J. 3 plants

Page 16

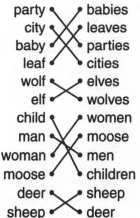

fox — foxes
ax — axes
box — boxes
bus — buses
dress — dresses
kiss — kisses
lunch — lunches
peach — peaches
inch — inches
bush — bushes
wish — wishes
ash — ashes

party — parties
city — cities
baby — babies
leaf — leaves
wolf — wolves
elf — elves
child — children
man — men
woman — women
moose — moose
deer — deer
sheep — sheep

FS-30041 Grammar

Answers

Page 17
1. friends
2. heat
3. spoon
4. bowls
5. cubes
6. spoons
7. seconds
8. minute

Page 18
The scenes in the picture depicting the following verbs should be colored: swings, balance, drinking, step, bow, follows. Written verbs will vary.

Page 19
1. am
2. is
3. am
4. is
5. are
6. are
7. Are
8. are
9. is
10. am

Page 20
1. is
2. live
3. make
4. hunt
5. eat
6. uses
7. sleep
8. have

Page 21

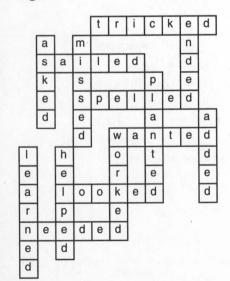

Page 22
write — thought
read — wrote
think — said
say — read

go — flew
run — ran
fly — went
swim — stood
ride — swam
stand — rode

eat — saw
drink — heard
see — ate
hear — drank
have — lost
lose — had

give — took
take — made
make — left
get — gave
leave — came
come — got

Page 23
1. left
2. rode
3. got
4. ran
5. sang
6. made
7. drew
8. wrote
9. gave
10. put
11. told
12. sat

Page 24
The scenes in the picture depicting the following adjectives (Wibbles) should be colored to match these adjectives: tall, round, bumpy, happy, sad, and young. Written adjectives will vary.

Page 26
short — taller — slowest
tall — slower — shortest
slow — shorter — fastest
fast — later — tallest
nice — faster — nicest
late — hotter — biggest
hot — sadder — latest
big — nicer — saddest
sad — bigger — hottest
happy — funnier — messiest
funny — messier — happiest
messy — happier — funniest

Page 27
1. an
2. a
3. a
4. a
5. a
6. a
7. a
8. an
9. a
10. an
11. a
12. an
13. a
14. an
15. an
16. a
17. a
18. a
19. a
20. a

Page 28
1. it
2. he
3. she
4. it
5. they
6. she
7. he
8. they
9. I
10. we

Page 29
1. us
2. it
3. them
4. me
5. him
6. her

Page 30
Answers will vary. Possible answers include:
1. quickly
2. loudly
3. neatly
4. carefully
5. badly
6. slowly
7. proudly
8. quietly
9. happily

FS-30041 Grammar